FIRST PAST THE POST®

Vocabulary in Context

Level 1

Published by University of Buckingham Press.
With special thanks to the children who tested our material at the Eleven Plus Exams centre in Harrow.

ISBN: 9781908684868

About Us

Eleven Plus Exams is the largest website in the UK that specifically prepares children for the 11 plus exams. The website offers a vast amount of information and advice on the 11 plus as well as a moderated online forum, books, downloadable material and online services to enhance your child's chances of success.

The company also provides specialist 11 plus tuition and is a supplier of online services to schools. Eleven Plus Exams is recognised as a trusted and authoritative source. It has been quoted in numerous national newspapers, including The Telegraph, The Observer, The Daily Mail and The Sunday Telegraph, as well as BBC Radio and national television (BBC1 and Channel 4).

Set up in 2004, the website grew from an initial 20 webpages to more than 65,000 today, and has been visited by millions of parents. The website gives impartial advice on exam preparation and techniques. It is moderated by over experts who provide support for parents both before and after the exams.

Visit our website and see why we are the market's leading one-stop shop for all your 11 plus needs.

- ✓ Comprehensive quality content and advice written by 11 plus experts
- ✓ Eleven Plus Exams online shop supplying a wide range of practice books, e-papers, software and apps
- ✓ Lots of FREE practice papers to download
- ✓ Professional tuition service
- ✓ Short revision courses
- ✓ Year-long 11 plus courses
- ✓ Mock exams tailored to reflect those of the main examining bodies

Other titles in the First Past The Post® Series

11+ Essentials Range of Books

VERBAL REASONING

ISBN	TITLE
9781908684288	Verbal Reasoning: Cloze Tests Book 1
9781908684356	Verbal Reasoning: Cloze Tests Book 2
9781908684639	Verbal Reasoning: Vocabulary Book 1 - Multiple Choice
9781908684783	Verbal Reasoning: Vocabulary Book 2 - Multiple Choice
9781908684844	Verbal Reasoning: Vocabulary Book 3 - Multiple Choice
9781908684646	Verbal Reasoning: Grammar and Spelling Book 1 - Multiple Choice
9781908684790	Verbal Reasoning: Grammar and Spelling Book 2 - Multiple Choice
9781908684868	Verbal Reasoning: Vocabulary in Context Level 1
9781908684875	Verbal Reasoning: Vocabulary in Context Level 2
9781908684882	Verbal Reasoning: Vocabulary in Context Level 3
9781908684899	Verbal Reasoning: Vocabulary in Context Level 4

ENGLISH

ISBN	TITLE
9781908684295	English: Comprehensions Book 1 Classic Literature
9781908684486	English: Comprehensions Book 2 Contemporary Literature
9781908684851	English: Comprehensions Book 3 Non-Fiction

NUMERICAL REASONING

ISBN	TITLE
9781908684431	Numerical Reasoning: Quick-Fire Book 1
9781908684448	Numerical Reasoning: Quick-Fire Book 2
9781908684653	Numerical Reasoning: Quick-Fire Book 1 - Multiple Choice
9781908684752	Numerical Reasoning: Quick-Fire Book 2 - Multiple Choice
9781908684301	Numerical Reasoning: Multi-Part Book 1
9781908684363	Numerical Reasoning: Multi-Part Book 2
9781908684769	Numerical Reasoning: Multi-Part Post 1 - Multiple Choice
9781908684776	Numerical Reasoning: Multi-Part Book 2 - Multiple Choice

MATHEMATICS

ISBN	TITLE
9781908684462	Maths: Mental Arithmetic Book 1
9781908684806	Maths: Worded Problems Book 1
9781908684936	Maths: Worded Problems Book 2
9781908684493	Maths Dictionary Plus

NON-VERBAL REASONING

ISBN	TITLE
9781908684318	3D Non-Verbal Reasoning Book 1
9781908684479	3D Non-Verbal Reasoning Book 2

PUZZLES

ISBN	TITLE
9781908684905	Puzzles: Maths Crosswords
9781908684912	Puzzles: Vocabulary

Test Paper Packs

ISBN	TITLE
9781908684103	English Practice Papers - Multiple Choice Pack 1
9781908684127	Verbal Reasoning Practice Papers - Multiple Choice Pack 1
9781908684134	Non-Verbal Reasoning Practice Papers - Multiple Choice Pack 1
9781908684110	Mathematics Practice Papers - Multiple Choice Pack 1

Contents

(1) # Example Exercise

Today's Words

(2)

bitterly	unsparingly	estate	traitors	defeated

Young Folks' History of England – Charlotte Yonge

(3) Edward was *bitterly* angry now. He sent on an army to deal *unsparingly* with the rising, and set out to follow with his son, now grown to man's *estate*. Crueller things than he had ever allowed before were done to the places where Robert Bruce had been acknowledged as king, and his friends were hung as *traitors* wherever they were found; but Bruce himself could not be caught. He was living a wild life among the lakes and hills; and Edward, who was an old man now, had been taken so ill at Carlisle, that he could not come on to keep his own strict rule among his men. All the winter he lay sick there; and in the spring he heard that Bruce, whom he thought quite crushed, had suddenly burst upon the English, *defeated* them, and was gathering strength every day.

(4) **Example Sentences** - Use today's words to complete the following sentences.

1. They would not believe a lowly servant over a man of such high

   _____

2. The Allied forces _____ Germany in World War II.

3. After she was betrayed by her only friend, she treated him very

   _____

4. It was common for _____ to be hanged, drawn and quartered.

   _____

5. He criticised the film _____ .

(5) **Definitions** - Write today's words next to their meanings.

1. In a way that shows anger, hurt or resentment   _____

2. A period, condition or state of ones life   _____

3. In a way that is merciless and severe   _____

4. To have overcome something or someone in a fight or contest

   _____

5. People who betray someone, something or their country

   _____

(6) Today's Idiom

> ***to put your foot in it***
> *to accidentally say something that upsets or embarrasses somebody*
> ***I put my foot in it by asking if she'd passed the test; she had not.***

How to use this book

Refer to the example opposite.

(1) **Do one exercise per day.** There are 50 exercises in this book and each book in the series. To best develop the skill of understanding vocabulary in context, we recommend you do no more than one exercise per day. It's also best to try them without using a dictionary.

(2) **Look at the words in the blue box.** These words are also italicised in blue in the passage. You are not expected to know what they mean, however, by reading the passage, the example sentences and the definitions, you should be able to work out the meaning.

(3) **Read the passage carefully.** As you are reading, try putting your thumb over any words you don't know and think about what words could be used instead. This is called the **'thumb rule'** and is a good starting pointing for working out the meaning of an unfamiliar word.

(4) **Complete the sample sentences.** Choose which word in the blue box fits best in the blank space. To help you, try and think about the context of the word in the passage and look at the definitions as well.

(5) **Complete the definitions.** Given the example sentences and the passage, write each word next to its definition, as fits best.

Once you have finished the exercises, check your answers. Don't worry if you don't get everything right first time. Just look back through the passage and example sentences to see whether you can now understand their context. Soon you will find working out the meaning of unfamiliar words much easier!

(6) **Read the idioms or word origin.** Idioms are phrases often used in conversations and stories, and word origins reveal the amazing number of languages that have influenced the English we use today. Being familiar with both, will expand your understanding of language and help to improve your comprehension skills.

Creative Writing Tips

How to use this book for creative writing practice

When reading the passages in this book, think about how you might continue the story. If you're stuck for ideas, here are some useful questions you can ask yourself:

- What is the character feeling? Would they celebrate, cry or shout?
- What would the characters do or say next? Would they go somewhere, or make a decision about something?
- Could you introduce a new character or event? Does it start pouring with rain, or does somebody come to visit?
- Is there an environment or setting you could describe? Does your story continue in a vast, expansive ocean, or could you describe the details of a room?

BLANK PAGE

Vocabulary in Context

Level 1

Each exercise in this book should take you around
10 minutes to complete.

Exercise 1

Today's Words

dazzled	studded	sparkling	tint	wondering

The Wonderful Wizard of Oz – L. Frank Baum

Even with eyes protected by the green spectacles, Dorothy and her friends were at first *dazzled* by the brilliancy of the wonderful City. The streets were lined with beautiful houses all built of green marble and *studded* everywhere with *sparkling* emeralds. They walked over a pavement of the same green marble, and where the blocks were joined together were rows of emeralds, set closely, and glittering in the brightness of the sun. The window panes were of green glass; even the sky above the City had a green *tint*, and the rays of the sun were green.

There were many people – men, women, and children – walking about, and these were all dressed in green clothes and had greenish skins. They looked at Dorothy and her strangely assorted company with *wondering* eyes, and the children all ran away and hid behind their mothers when they saw the Lion; but no one spoke to them.

Example Sentences - Use today's words to complete the following sentences.

1. There she was, with _____ eyes and wavy hair, exactly how he remembered her.
2. The cupcakes were _____ with iced gems for decoration.
3. The audience was _____ by the spectacular performance.
4. She died her hair red with just a _____ of pink.
5. She often found herself _____ about the origin of the solar system.

Definitions - Write today's words next to their meanings.

1. Feeling admiration or curiosity; considering _____
2. A small amount of a colour _____
3. Covered in several small, protruding objects _____
4. Shining brightly with flashes of light _____
5. Overwhelmed by intense light or awe _____

Today's Word Origin

pest
*The word originates from the Latin word **pestis** meaning 'plague'.*

2

Exercise 2

Today's Words

rusty	loose	bare	lovely	shone

The Snow Queen – Hans Christian Andersen

The door was shut, but she shook the *rusty* latch till it came *loose* and the door sprang open. And then little Gerda ran in her *bare* feet into the wide world. Three times she looked back, but there was nobody following her. At last she couldn't run any longer and sat down on a big stone; and when she looked round she found that summer had gone and it was late autumn. You couldn't tell in the *lovely* garden, where the sun always *shone* and there were every season's flowers.

Example Sentences - Use today's words to complete the following sentences.

1. She unfastened her sandals and sunk her _____ feet into the sand.
2. The ribbon on her hair came undone and her hair fell _____ .
3. The lock had been unused for so long that it had become _____ .
4. For the whole afternoon the weather had been _____ , just perfect for a picnic.
5. The spotlight _____ down on centre stage, waiting for the singer to appear.

Definitions - Write today's words next to their meanings.

1. Affected by or covered in rust _____
2. Gave out a bright light _____
3. Not covered _____
4. Not tight, compact or tied in place _____
5. Very nice, delightful _____

Today's Idiom

to be a bit rusty
to be not as good as you used to be at a skill or subject

His cooking skills were a bit rusty but the dish was immaculate.

Exercise 3

Today's Words

shimmering	mild	stirring	rigging	cabin

The Little Mermaid – Hans Christian Andersen

The sun had just set when she raised her head above the surface, but all the clouds were *shimmering* like roses and gold, and in the middle of the pink sky the evening star shone out brightly and beautifully; the air was soft and *mild*, and the sea dead calm. A big ship lay there, with three masts, and only one sail up, for not a wind was *stirring*; and sailors were sitting in the *rigging* and on the yard-arms. There was sound of music and singing; and as the evening drew on, a hundred coloured lanterns were lit: it looked as though the flags of every nation were waving in the air. The little mermaid swam right up to the *cabin* window; and each time the waves lifted her up she could see in through the crystal-clear panes to where many well-dressed people were standing.

Example Sentences - Use today's words to complete the following sentences.

1. The pirate climbed down to the main deck using the ship's _____ .
2. The gentle waves were _____ in the evening sunlight.
3. The front _____ of an aeroplane is usually where passengers with the more expensive tickets sit.
4. The giant oak tree's leaves were _____ in the gentle evening breeze.
5. Luckily, the weather had remained _____ for the week they were on holiday.

Definitions - Write today's words next to their meanings.

1. Moving (slightly)   _____
2. Moderately warm   _____
3. The system of ropes that support a ship's masts   _____
4. Shining with a soft, wavering light   _____
5. A private room or compartment   _____

Today's Word Origin

toxic
*The word originates from the medieval Latin word **toxicus** meaning 'poisoned',*
*which comes from the Greek phrase **toxikon** 'poison for arrows'.*

Exercise 4

disagreeable	bogs	muddy	wilder	underbrush

The Wonderful Wizard of Oz – L. Frank Baum

After climbing down from the china wall the travellers found themselves in a *disagreeable* country, full of *bogs* and marshes and covered with tall, rank grass. It was difficult to walk without falling into *muddy* holes, for the grass was so thick that it hid them from sight. However, by carefully picking their way, they got safely along until they reached solid ground. But here the country seemed *wilder* than ever, and after a long and tiresome walk through the *underbrush* they entered another forest, where the trees were bigger and older than any they had ever seen.

Example Sentences - Use today's words to complete the following sentences.

1. The woods were surrounded by a thick _____ .
2. My mother dislikes my aunt and finds her very _____ .
3. My dog was much _____ when we got him, but now he is very well behaved.
4. The wetlands were beautiful but contained a number of _____ into which we fell several times.
5. Wellies are best for wearing when walking along _____ paths with lots of puddles.

Definitions - Write today's words next to their meanings.

1. More untamed (unused land in its natural state) _____
2. Covered in dirt _____
3. Unenjoyable or unpleasant _____
4. Areas of wet, soft, muddy ground _____
5. Shrubs and small trees forming the undergrowth in a forest _____

Today's Idiom

to break the ice
to make an awkward situation feel more relaxed

Meeting people can be scary, so I like to break the ice with a joke.

Exercise 5

Today's Words

| eventful | ditch | divided | jagged | steep |

The Wonderful Wizard of Oz – L. Frank Baum

This was to be an *eventful* day for the travellers. They had hardly been walking an hour when they saw before them a great *ditch* that crossed the road and *divided* the forest as far as they could see on either side. It was a very wide ditch, and when they crept up to the edge and looked into it they could see it was also very deep, and there were many big, *jagged* rocks at the bottom. The sides were so *steep* that none of them could climb down, and for a moment it seemed that their journey must end.

Example Sentences - Use today's words to complete the following sentences.

1. The controversial issue had _____ the community.
2. The glass broke, and he cut his finger on its _____ edge.
3. The car swerved from the road and into a deep _____ .
4. I wish I was fit enough to climb the _____ slope leading to my house, without getting out of breath.
5. The parents sat back with a sigh; it had been an _____ day out.

Definitions - Write today's words next to their meanings.

1. With sharp points protruding   _____
2. A narrow channel at the side of a road or field   _____
3. Rising sharply   _____
4. Marked by interesting events   _____
5. Separated into parts   _____

Today's Word Origin

acid
*The word originates from the Latin word **acidus** meaning 'sour-tasting'.*

6

Exercise 6

Today's Words

pleasant	bent	strapped	ought	temper

The Wind in the Willows – Kenneth Grahame

Packing the basket was not quite such *pleasant* work as unpacking the basket. It never is. But the Mole was *bent* on enjoying everything, and although just when he had got the basket packed and *strapped* up tightly he saw a plate staring up at him from the grass, and when the job had been done again the Rat pointed out a fork which anybody *ought* to have seen, and last of all, behold! the mustard-pot, which he had been sitting on without knowing it – still, somehow, the thing got finished at last, without much loss of *temper*.

Example Sentences - Use today's words to complete the following sentences.

1. The sailor was _____ on sailing round the world alone.
2. The weather was _____ enough to enjoy a picnic by the lakeside.
3. She knew that she _____ to go to bed now, but she was desperate to finish her book.
4. The luggage was _____ tightly to the roof of the car so that it wouldn't fall off.
5. The teacher lost his _____ when his class misbehaved.

Definitions - Write today's words next to their meanings.

1. Should, out of duty or correctness _____
2. Determined to achieve something _____
3. A tendency to become angry _____
4. Fastened or secured with straps _____
5. Likeable, enjoyable _____

┌─ **Today's Idiom** ─────────────────────────────────┐

to get somebody off your back
to make someone stop disturbing or pestering you

Mum didn't get off my back about homework until she saw me do it.

└──┘

Exercise 7

Today's Words

| content | grown | scratch | roosted | dirty |

The Jungle Book – Rudyard Kipling

Now you must be *content* to skip ten or eleven whole years, and only guess at all the wonderful life that Mowgli led among the wolves, because if it were written out it would fill ever so many books. He grew up with the cubs, though they of course were *grown* wolves almost before he was a child, and Father Wolf taught him business, and the meaning of things in the jungle, till every rustle in the grass, every breath of the warm night air, every note of the owls above his head, every *scratch* of a bat's claws as it *roosted* for a while in a tree, and every splash of every little fish jumping in a pool, meant just as much to him as the work of his office means to a business man. When he was not learning he sat out in the sun and slept, and ate, and went to sleep again; when he felt *dirty* or hot he swam in the forest pools; and when he wanted honey (Baloo told him that honey and nuts were just as pleasant to eat as raw meat) he climbed up for it, and that Bagheera showed him how to do.

Example Sentences - Use today's words to complete the following sentences.

1. He kept his childhood teddy until he was a _____ man with children of his own.
2. The kitchen was very _____ , unwashed plates lay everywhere.
3. Her mother impressed upon her daughter the importance of learning to be _____ with what she had.
4. The flock of parakeets _____ in the tall trees.
5. Although the kitten was remarkably cute, it was likely to give you a _____ .

Definitions - Write today's words next to their meanings.

1. Unclean, soiled   _____
2. A score or mark on the surface of something   _____
3. Satisfied, not unhappy   _____
4. Arrived at full maturity   _____
5. Settled for rest or sleep (birds)   _____

Today's Word Origin

malice
*The word originates from the Latin word **malus** meaning 'bad'.*

Exercise 8

Today's Words

| inky | markings | bold | reckless | wounded |

The Jungle Book – Rudyard Kipling

A black shadow dropped down into the circle. It was Bagheera, the Black Panther, *inky* black all over, but with the panther *markings* showing up in certain lights like the pattern of watered silk. Everybody knew Bagheera, and nobody cared to cross his path; for he was as cunning as Tabaqui, as *bold* as the wild buffalo, and as *reckless* as the *wounded* elephant. But he had a voice as soft as wild honey dripping from a tree, and a skin softer than down.

Example Sentences - Use today's words to complete the following sentences.

1. He was known for climbing trees, running across roads and other _____ behaviour.
2. She decided to make the _____ move of asking him out for dinner.
3. She looked up into the _____ blackness of the night sky.
4. After the battle, many soldiers lay _____ on the desolate battlefield.
5. The _____ of every tiger are unique, like a fingerprint.

Definitions - Write today's words next to their meanings.

1. Physically injured   _____
2. Dark blue or black   _____
3. Confident, courageous   _____
4. A pattern of marks on an animal's fur, feathers or skin   _____
5. Careless, with no care for danger   _____

Today's Idiom

to get out of the wrong side of the bed
to be moody and bad-tempered

She's fuming, I think she got out of the wrong side of the bed this morning.

Exercise 9

substantial	hamper	ordinary	outstanding	creative

A School Fête

There were easily 100 stalls in the big sports hall of the school, each of which had been conceived, designed and realised by the two or three students who stood efficiently running them. There were *substantial* prizes on offer for the best stalls, including a trip to the theatre, a trip to an amusement park, and a huge picnic *hamper*. All the students had put in a great deal of effort, making signs and games for the visitors to play and look at. Mostly, the prizes the students had brought for the winners of their games were *ordinary* – sweets or chocolate – but the standard of the games themselves was *outstanding*. Everyone had been hugely imaginative and *creative*, and it looked as if everyone deserved to win.

Example Sentences - Use today's words to complete the following sentences.

1. The achievement of the British Olympic team was _____ .
2. Is was just an _____ day at the office, nothing unusual happened.
3. Children are usually more _____ than adults.
4. For Christmas, he received a large _____ filled with food and wine.
5. _____ effort was required to get the shy boy up onto the stage.

Definitions - Write today's words next to their meanings.

1. A basket containing food or other gift items _____
2. With no special features, normal _____
3. Significant, of some size or worth _____
4. Having original or imaginative ideas _____
5. Exceptional or noticeable _____

Today's Word Origin

port
The word originates from the Latin word **portus** *meaning 'haven or harbour'.*

Exercise 10

Today's Words

sociable	stresses	festive	snug	lavish

Christmas Time

In my house, the month of December is a very *sociable* time of year. The whole family gathers together to celebrate, exchange gifts and spend time with one another. Spending time with family and friends is good for the soul because it allows everyone to forget their everyday *stresses* and remember what is truly important. Everyone works together to decorate the Christmas tree, which always ends up looking very *festive*. The weather outside is usually bitterly cold, but inside it is *snug* and warm, with hot fires and woollen jumpers. Christmas dinner is traditionally a *lavish* meal, with lots of dishes and more food than anyone could possibly eat.

Example Sentences - Use today's words to complete the following sentences.

1. The emperor's palace was _____ , the walls were covered in beautiful tapestries, and every surface was golden and encrusted with jewels.
2. Sometimes the _____ of a busy day can only be erased by a hot bubble bath.
3. He was a very _____ child, and loved to be with his friends.
4. My feet were nice and _____ since my boots were lined with fur.
5. The atmosphere was very _____ , everyone was laughing and dancing.

Definitions - Write today's words next to their meanings.

1. Things that cause strain or tiredness   _____
2. Relating to a celebration or cheerful event   _____
3. Rich, elaborate, extravagant   _____
4. Willing to talk and engage with other people   _____
5. Warm and cosy _____

> **Today's Idiom**
>
> **a breath of fresh air**
> *a person or thing that is new and different in a good way*
>
> ***After studying the Tudors for a whole term, science was a breath of fresh air.***

Exercise 11

Today's Words

sane	majority	educated	distinct	virtuous

Crime: Its Cause and Treatment – Clarence Darrow

There can be no *sane* discussion of "crime" and "criminals" without an investigation of the meaning of the words. A large *majority* of men, even among the *educated*, speak of a "criminal" as if the word had a clearly defined meaning and as if men were divided by a plain and *distinct* line into the criminal and the *virtuous*. As a matter of fact, there is no such division, and from the nature of things, there never can be such a line.

Example Sentences - Use today's words to complete the following sentences.

1. No _____ person could possibly expect a child to go to school when they are sick.
2. He was the most honest and _____ person I had ever met.
3. There was a _____ difference between the behaviour of the two children.
4. The _____ of people living in Britain are under the age of 70.
5. The princess was clearly _____ , as she had an excellent understanding of world history.

Definitions - Write today's words next to their meanings.

1. Most, more than half _____
2. Having high moral standards, being good _____
3. Clear and obvious _____
4. Sensible, reasonable _____
5. Having a formal education _____

Today's Word Origin

barbarian
*The word originates from the Greek word **barbaros** meaning 'foreign'.*

Exercise 12

Today's Words

rich	medieval	residence	grievous	monk

A Local History

The land around the stately home was *rich* in history and mythology. The hill on which it stood had once been the site of a *medieval* monastery. Only one small part of the original building remained - that of a small prison. The story went that the prison had been the *residence* of a criminal, locked up there for 30 years, as punishment for the *grievous* crime of killing a fellow *monk*.

Example Sentences - Use today's words to complete the following sentences.

1. On her school trip, Kerry visited a _____ castle, built in 895 A.D.
2. The discovery was made by a _____ visiting from a temple in Tibet.
3. The land was _____ in natural minerals, which meant it was highly sought after.
4. The old house was the _____ of two sisters.
5. He made a _____ error when he walked into the dark woods alone.

Definitions - Write today's words next to their meanings.

1. A member of a religious community of men _____
2. Serious, regrettable _____
3. A living space _____
4. Relating to the Middle Ages _____
5. Having a particular thing in large amounts _____

Today's Idiom

to turn a deaf ear to something
to ignore or refuse to listen to what somebody is telling you

Every time Dad asked us to do chores, we turned a deaf ear.

Exercise 13

Today's Words

expedition	shrubbery	rustle	decay	steadily

The Hound of the Baskervilles – Arthur Conan Doyle

In five minutes we were outside the door, starting upon our *expedition*. We hurried through the dark *shrubbery*, amid the dull moaning of the autumn wind and the *rustle* of the falling leaves. The night air was heavy with the smell of damp and *decay*. Now and again the moon peeped out for an instant, but clouds were driving over the face of the sky, and just as we came out on the moor a thin rain began to fall. The light still burned *steadily* in front.

Example Sentences - Use today's words to complete the following sentences.

1. The gardener was proud of her _____ and flowerbeds.
2. Imogen looked _____ into the beast's eyes. "Sit!" she said.
3. The _____ would take them to the highest point of the mountain.
4. A slight _____ came from the bushes at the edge of the garden.
5. It was sad to see such a lovely bunch of flowers _____ .

Definitions - Write today's words next to their meanings.

1. To make a soft, muffled crackling sound _____
2. In a regular, controlled manner _____
3. An area planted with bushy plants _____
4. Rotting or decomposition _____
5. A journey undertaken with a particular purpose _____

Today's Word Origin

alphabet
*The word originates from the Greek word **alphabētos** meaning 'alphabet',
combining the first two letters of the Greek alphabet, **alpha** and **beta**.*

Exercise 14

Today's Words

succeeded	puzzled	provoking	furrow	conclusion

Alice's Adventures in Wonderland – Lewis Carroll

The chief difficulty Alice found at first was in managing her flamingo; she *succeeded* in getting its body tucked away, comfortably enough, under her arm, with its legs hanging down, but generally, just as she had got its neck nicely straightened out, and was going to give the hedgehog a blow with its head, it would twist itself round and look up in her face, with such a *puzzled* expression that she could not help bursting out laughing: and when she had got its head down, and was going to begin again, it was very *provoking* to find that the hedgehog had unrolled itself, and was in the act of crawling away: besides all this, there was generally a ridge or a *furrow* in the way wherever she wanted to send the hedgehog to, and, as the doubled-up soldiers were always getting up and walking off to other parts of the ground, Alice soon came to the *conclusion* that it was a very difficult game indeed.

Example Sentences - Use today's words to complete the following sentences.

1. The boy glanced at her with a _____ look on his face.
2. To help the water reach the seeds, the farmer ploughed a _____ next to each row.
3. After a long discussion, the team came to the _____ that they would forfeit the match.
4. I _____ in convincing my mother to get a dog. We named it Bingo.
5. Lisa enjoyed _____ her brother.

Definitions - Write today's words next to their meanings.

1. The final decision or result   _____
2. Achieved the desired result   _____
3. A long narrow trench made in the ground   _____
4. Perplexed, unable to understand something   _____
5. Causing annoyance   _____

Today's Idiom

to be barking up the wrong tree
to seek answers in the wrong place

"You're barking up the wrong tree, of course I didn't eat your birthday cake."

Exercise 15

Today's Words

pattering	trotting	savage	timid	violently

Alice's Adventures in Wonderland – Lewis Carroll

After a time she heard a little *pattering* of feet in the distance, and she hastily dried her eyes to see what was coming. It was the White Rabbit returning, splendidly dressed, with a pair of white kid gloves in one hand and a large fan in the other: he came *trotting* along in a great hurry, muttering to himself as he came, "Oh! the Duchess, the Duchess! Oh! won't she be *savage* if I've kept her waiting!" Alice felt so desperate that she was ready to ask help of any one; so, when the Rabbit came near her, she began, in a low, *timid* voice, "If you please, sir –" The Rabbit started *violently*, dropped the white kid gloves and the fan, and scurried away into the darkness as hard as he could go.

Example Sentences - Use today's words to complete the following sentences.

1. The _____ boy hid behind his elder sister as they entered the crowded room.
2. The only sound that could be heard was the _____ of raindrops against the window.
3. Michael coughed _____ as he lay in bed for the third day in a row.
4. The horse was _____ along the street, excited to get back to his stables.
5. Lena was terrified of the _____ dog, which guarded the house next-door.

Definitions - Write today's words next to their meanings.

1. A quick, light tapping noise _____
2. Fierce, ferocious _____
3. Shy, lacking courage _____
4. In a strong, vigorous manner _____
5. Moving faster than a walk but slower than a run _____

Today's Word Origin

superficial
*The word originates from the Latin word **superficies** meaning 'surface'.*

Exercise 16

Today's Words

advice	scolded	croquet	fond	pretending

Alice's Adventures in Wonderland – Lewis Carroll

She generally gave herself very good *advice* (though she very seldom followed it), and sometimes she *scolded* herself so severely as to bring tears into her eyes; and once she remembered trying to box her own ears for having cheated herself in a game of *croquet* she was playing against herself, for this curious child was very *fond* of *pretending* to be two people. "But it's no use now," thought poor Alice, "to pretend to be two people! Why there's hardly enough of me left to make one respectable person!"

Example Sentences - Use today's words to complete the following sentences.

1. The twins were very mischievous and enjoyed _____ to be each other.

2. Having ten brothers, Michael was never short of well-meaning

    _____ .

3. Jamie wanted to play a game of _____ with her friends.

4. The mother _____ her son for breaking his new toy.

5. Jane's grandfather was very _____ of the family dog, and would often talk to it.

Definitions - Write today's words next to their meanings.

1. Having an affection or liking for someone or something   _____

2. Imitating or playing at   _____

3. An outdoor game in which players use mallets to drive wooden balls through hoops

    _____

4. Guidance, a recommendation   _____

5. Angrily told off   _____

Today's Idiom

to see eye to eye with somebody
to agree with someone or have similar opinions

Supporting the same team was the only thing they saw eye to eye on.

Exercise 17

mortal	exceedingly	bore	polished	blushing

The Heroes; Or, Greek Fairy Tales For My Children – Charles Kingsley

There came a lady to him through the wood, taller than he, or any *mortal* man; but beautiful *exceedingly*, with great grey eyes, clear and piercing, but strangely soft and mild. On her head was a helmet, and in her hand a spear. And over her shoulder, above her long blue robes, hung a goat-skin, which *bore* up a mighty shield of brass, *polished* like a mirror. She stood and looked at him with her clear grey eyes; and Perseus saw that her eye-lids never moved, nor her eyeballs, but looked straight through and through him, and into his very heart, as if she could see all the secrets of his soul, and knew all that he had ever thought or longed for since the day that he was born. And Perseus dropped his eyes, trembling and *blushing*, as the wonderful lady spoke.

Example Sentences - Use today's words to complete the following sentences.

1. The shoe-maker _____ all the shoes in her shop, ready to be sold in the morning.

2. The woman _____ all her possessions in a large sack on her back.

3. The gods and heroes would often watch the _____ men who lived on earth.

4. John was _____ because he had just been complemented on his good looks.

5. I was _____ delighted by the news that my sister was coming to stay.

Definitions - Write today's words next to their meanings.

1. Shiny as a result of being rubbed   _____

2. Carried, past tense of the verb to bear   _____

3. Subject to death, human   _____

4. To a great extent, very   _____

5. Becoming pink in the face   _____

Today's Word Origin

iceberg
*The word originates from the Dutch word **ijsberg**. **Ijs** means 'ice' and **berg** means 'hill'.*

Exercise 18

Today's Words

proclaimed	lords	oaths	meek	obedient

Young Folks' History of England – Charlotte Yonge

The poor little baby, Henry VI, was but nine months old when—over the grave of his father in England, and his grandfather in France—he was *proclaimed* King of France and England. The crown of England was held over his head, and his *lords* made their *oaths* to him: and when he was nine years old he was sent to Paris, and there crowned King of France. He was a very good, little, gentle boy, as *meek* and *obedient* as possible; but his friends, who knew that a king must be brave, strong, and firm for his people's sake, began to be afraid that nothing would ever make him manly.

Example Sentences - Use today's words to complete the following sentences.

1. My last pet dog was so _____ and always did what he was told.
2. The little girl was _____ and quiet, and went along with whatever the other children suggested.
3. The _____ were able to control the land without much interference from the King.
4. Arthur _____ that from now on only boys could play in the tree house.
5. The bride and groom made _____ to love, honour and protect one another.

Definitions - Write today's words next to their meanings.

1. Announced officially _____
2. Solemn promises made in front of witnesses _____
3. One who follows, or is willing to follow instructions _____
4. People of noble birth, often with a great deal of authority _____
5. Quiet, gentle and submissive _____

Today's Idiom

a false alarm

when people wrongly believe that something dangerous or bad will happen

The dog hadn't actually run away, it was a false alarm.

Exercise 19

Today's Words

| trailing | velvet | embroidered | fastened | honour |

The Viking Tales – Jennie Hall

The queen wore a *trailing* dress of blue *velvet* with long flowing sleeves. She had a short apron of striped Arabian silk with gold fringe along the bottom. From her shoulders hung a long train of scarlet wool *embroidered* in gold. White linen covered her head. Her long yellow hair was pulled around at the sides and over her breast and was *fastened* under the belt of her apron. As she walked, her train made a pleasant rustle among the pine branches. She was tall and straight and strong. Some of her younger women wore no linen on their heads and had their white arms bare, with bracelets shining on them. They, too, were tall and strong.

All the time men were calling across the fire to one another asking news or telling jokes and laughing. An old man, Harald's uncle, sat in the high seat on the north side. That was the place of *honour*.

Example Sentences - Use today's words to complete the following sentences.

1. The man gazed admiringly at the _____ detail on the corner of the handkerchief, so lovingly sewed.
2. The king entered with a great fanfare and his long cape _____ behind him.
3. She touched the softness of the heavy _____ curtain.
4. He didn't want to lose the key, so he _____ it to a chain on his bag.
5. He was the guest of _____ at his birthday meal.

Definitions - Write today's words next to their meanings.

1. High respect   _____
2. A woven fabric that has a thick layer of many small threads on one side

   _____
3. Stitched and decorated with thread   _____
4. Drawn along behind   _____
5. Attached, hooked   _____

Today's Word Origin

bomb
*The word originates from the Greek word **bombos** meaning 'booming, humming'.*

Exercise 20

Today's Words

| hunt | tend | flitted | curled | beams |

The Viking Tales – Jennie Hall

Iceland is a little country far north in the cold sea. Men found it and went there to live more than a thousand years ago. During the warm season they used to fish and make fish-oil and *hunt* sea-birds and gather feathers and *tend* their sheep and make hay. But the winters were long and dark and cold. Men and women and children stayed in the house and carded and spun and wove and knit. A whole family sat for hours around the fire in the middle of the room. That fire gave the only light. Shadows *flitted* in the dark corners. Smoke *curled* along the high *beams* in the ceiling. The children sat on the dirt floor close by the fire. The grown people were on a long narrow bench that they had pulled up to the light and warmth. Everybody's hands were busy with wool. The work left their minds free to think and their lips to talk. What was there to talk about? The summer's fishing, the killing of a fox, a voyage to Norway.

Example Sentences - Use today's words to complete the following sentences.

1. The man took his bow and arrow into the forest to _____ .
2. I stayed at home to _____ to my new baby sister.
3. The ceiling of the cottage was supported by thick wooden _____ .
4. Long, green tendrils grew up the walls and _____ around the window frames.
5. The birds _____ about in the trees above.

Definitions - Write today's words next to their meanings.

1. Formed into a curved or spiral shape   _____
2. To care for or look after   _____
3. To chase and kill wild animals   _____
4. Long, sturdy pieces of wood or metal used to support the roof of a building _____
5. Moved swiftly and lightly   _____

Today's Idiom

to fight fire with fire
to use the same methods as your opponent in a contest or fight

After learning he had cheated, she fought fire with fire and cheated as well.

Exercise 21

Today's Words

cocoa	devoted	resisted	feebly	praised

The Magic City – Edith Nesbit

Then the children had a cocoa-and-date breakfast. (All expeditions seem to live mostly on *cocoa*, and when they come back they often write to the cocoa makers to say how good it was and they don't know what they would have done without it.) And the noble and *devoted* dogs licked and licked and licked, and the paint began to come off the lions' legs like anything. It was heavy work turning the lions over so as to get at the other or unlicked side, but the expedition worked with a will, and the lions *resisted* but *feebly*, being still asleep, and, besides, weak from loss of paint. And the dogs had a drink given them and were patted and *praised*, and set to work again. And they licked and licked for hours and hours.

Example Sentences - Use today's words to complete the following sentences.

1. The student was _____ for his neat handwriting.
2. The young girl called so _____ from the back of the room, that no one heard her.
3. There is nothing like a steaming mug of _____ after a long walk in the snow.
4. Both husband and wife were _____ to each other.
5. The man _____ the urge to laugh, because he didn't want to hurt her feelings.

Definitions - Write today's words next to their meanings.

1. In a way that is weak and without power _____
2. Hot chocolate drink _____
3. Fought back against someone or something _____
4. Entirely loyal to _____
5. Given admiration or approval _____

Today's Word Origin

hello
*The word originates as a variant from the earlier words **hollo** and **holloo**, both of which were cries used to urge on hunting dogs.*

Exercise 22

Today's Words

| eruption | awesome | ash | molten | inhabitants |

A Volcanic Disaster

In 79 AD the *eruption* of the volcano, Mount Vesuvius, destroyed several Roman settlements, including Pompeii and Herculaneum. Historians learned about the details of the eruption from the eyewitness account of Pliny the Younger, a Roman administrator and poet, who observed this *awesome* sight. A cloud of volcanic gas, stones and *ash*, 33 kilometres high, poured out from the top of the mountain. Herculaneum was destroyed by fast-moving *molten* lava which flowed down the mountain at 1.5 million tons per second. Pompeii, however, was destroyed by the ash, which fell so fast, most of the *inhabitants* were killed before they had a chance to disperse.

Example Sentences - Use today's words to complete the following sentences.

1. The _____ spectacle left the audience mesmerised.
2. The town was destroyed by a volcanic _____ in the year 2005.
3. The baker filled the cake with _____ chocolate.
4. After the explosion, a layer of _____ covered the landscape.
5. When the fire drill was over, all the _____ of the building were left standing outside.

Definitions - Write today's words next to their meanings.

1. Melted by heat _____
2. The powdery residue left after burning something _____
3. Extremely affecting, impressive or inspiring _____
4. The ultimate action of a live volcano _____
5. People or beings living in a place _____

Today's Idiom

to be ones own flesh and blood
to be a member of your own family

I treated the orphan boy like he was my own flesh and blood.

Exercise 23

Today's Words

giddy	glimpses	jerk	escort	limbs

The Jungle Book – Rudyard Kipling

Two of the strongest monkeys caught Mowgli under the arms and swung off with him through the tree-tops, twenty feet at a bound. Had they been alone they could have gone twice as fast, but the boy's weight held them back. Sick and *giddy* as Mowgli was he could not help enjoying the wild rush, though the *glimpses* of earth far down below frightened him, and the terrible check and *jerk* at the end of the swing over nothing but empty air brought his heart between his teeth.

His *escort* would rush him up a tree till he felt the weak topmost branches crackle and bend under them, and, then, with a cough and a whoop, would fling themselves into the air outward and downward, and bring up hanging by their hands or their feet to the lower *limbs* of the next tree.

Example Sentences - Use today's words to complete the following sentences.

1. She clambered onto the oak tree, and sat on one of the larger lower
   _____ .
2. As the aeroplane neared the airport, tantalising _____ of the city could be seen between the clouds.
3. She gave his arm a quick _____ to let him know it was time to leave.
4. The president was given a police _____ to accompany him to the hotel.
5. He felt _____ after several spins of the roundabout in the playground.

Definitions - Write today's words next to their meanings.

1. Person or group accompanying someone for protection   _____
2. Seeing something briefly or partially   _____
3. Branches of a tree   _____
4. A quick, sudden movement   _____
5. Dizzy, a sensation of whirling   _____

Today's Word Origin

naughty
*The word originates from the Old English word **naught**, meaning 'nothing', which originally meant 'possessing nothing, poor, needy'.*

Exercise 24

Today's Words

draughty	dragged	dear	wonders	shivered

The Railway Children – Edith Nesbit

They woke up, cold and melancholy, and stood shivering on the *draughty* platform while the baggage was taken out of the train. Then the engine, puffing and blowing, set to work again, and *dragged* the train away. The children watched the tail-lights of the guard's van disappear into the darkness.

This was the first train the children saw on that railway which was in time to become so very *dear* to them. They did not guess then how they would grow to love the railway, and how soon it would become the centre of their new life, nor what *wonders* and changes it would bring to them. They only *shivered* and sneezed and hoped the walk to the new house would not be long.

Example Sentences - Use today's words to complete the following sentences.

1. He was looking forward to all the _____ that awaited him in the new land.
2. The boy loved his toy car and _____ it with him everywhere.
3. My room is very _____ because there is a large gap under the door.
4. Despite their warm clothes and the roaring bonfire, they _____ as they watched the fireworks.
5. My best friend is very _____ to me and I shall miss her very much when she moves.

Definitions - Write today's words next to their meanings.

1. Pulled along behind _____
2. Close, thought of with deep affection _____
3. Things that are regarded as remarkable _____
4. Characterised by currents of cold air _____
5. Shook as a result of being cold _____

Today's Idiom

a goody two-shoes
a person who behaves well in order to be seen to please other people, e.g. teachers

He was the biggest bully at school, but in class he was a goody two-shoes.

Exercise 25

Today's Words

possessions	buried	tombs	prepare	achieve

The Pyramids

When the pharaohs of ancient Egypt died, their bodies, along with their most valued *possessions*, were *buried* in special *tombs* called pyramids. People thought that a proper burial ritual would *prepare* them for life after death. The Great Pyramid of Giza is the largest of the Egyptian pyramids, and was built by Pharaoh Khufu. It is acknowledged that he would only have been able to *achieve* this by using an enormous number of slaves.

Example Sentences - Use today's words to complete the following sentences.

1. Before moving house, they packed up all their _____ into boxes.
2. I always try to _____ the best mark that I can.
3. Bluebeard _____ his treasure under a large palm tree.
4. To _____ for her English exam, she read through all her notes from class.
5. They visited the _____ of soldiers who had died in the Great War.

Definitions - Write today's words next to their meanings.

1. To succeed in bringing about a specific goal _____
2. Monuments in or under which lie the remains of the dead _____
3. Hidden underground _____
4. To make ready _____
5. Things that are owned _____

Today's Word Origin

duke
The word originates from the Latin noun **dux** meaning 'leader', and the verb **ducere** meaning 'to lead'.

© 2017 ElevenPlusExams.co.uk   26   COPYING STRICTLY PROHIBITED

Exercise 26

Today's Words

squeal	sigh	fading	retired	bittersweet

Retirement

The big, red bus pulled into the station with a *squeal* and a *sigh*. For fifteen years it had made the same journey past the same houses and along the same roads. Its paint was *fading* and its seats were packed with dust. Mr Hobbes switched off the engine and stepped down from the driving seat for the last time. Today was the day the bus *retired* from service. He knew he would now get to drive a nice new vehicle, with a big engine and shiny new paint, but for Hobbes the moment was *bittersweet*. They had taken the journey together, all these years, and now it was time to part.

Example Sentences - Use today's words to complete the following sentences.

1. The lines on the road were _____ and becoming difficult to make out.
2. He had _____ from his job some years earlier and now had lots of time to see his grandchildren.
3. Returning to the house was _____ , it was a place of a happier times, now passed.
4. The girl let out an excited _____ when she caught sight of her presents.
5. "Oh, very well then, if you must," said Granny, with a _____ .

Definitions - Write today's words next to their meanings.

1. Losing colour, brightness or clarity   _____
2. A mixture of pleasure and sadness   _____
3. A high-pitched cry or noise   _____
4. To emit a long, deep, audible breath   _____
5. Having withdrawn from one's job and ceased to work   _____

Today's Idiom

to jump to conclusions
to make up one's mind about something without having enough information

I jumped to conclusions when I saw you holding the watch I had lost.

Exercise 27

Today's Words

| chestnut | plainly | unsteady | hopeless | dull |

Black Beauty – Anna Sewell

One day, while our cab and many others were waiting outside one of the parks where the music was playing, a shabby old cab drove up beside ours. The horse was an old worn-out *chestnut*, with an ill-kept coat, and bones that showed *plainly* through it, the knees knuckled over, and the fore-legs were very *unsteady*. I had been eating some hay, and the wind rolled a little lock of it that way, and the poor creature put out her long neck and picked it up, and then turned and looked about for more. There was a *hopeless* look in the *dull* eye that I could not help noticing, and then, as I was thinking where I had seen that horse before, she looked full at me and said, "Black Beauty, is that you?"

Example Sentences - Use today's words to complete the following sentences.

1. My baby brother has learned to walk but is still very _____ on his feet.

2. No matter how hard we tried to find a solution, the situation was clearly

   _____ .

3. The pony they chose was a young _____ with a beautiful rich brown coat.

4. I could _____ see the ice-cream on her blouse, however, I felt too awkward to mention it.

5. The sky was a _____ grey all day.

Definitions - Write today's words next to their meanings.

1. Easily seen _____
2. Without hope, desperate _____
3. Prone to fall, not stable _____
4. Without light, vividness or shine _____
5. A horse that is a brown colour, like some nuts _____

Today's Word Origin

plate
*The word originates from the Greek word **platus** meaning 'flat' but more recently from the medieval Latin word **plata** meaning 'plate armour'.*

Exercise 28

Today's Words

circumstance	mist	cry	cantered	beyond

Black Beauty – Anna Sewell

Before I was two years old a *circumstance* happened which I have never forgotten. It was early in the spring; there had been a little frost in the night, and a light *mist* still hung over the woods and meadows. I and the other colts were feeding at the lower part of the field when we heard, quite in the distance, what sounded like the *cry* of dogs. The oldest of the colts raised his head, pricked his ears, and said, "There are the hounds!" and immediately *cantered* off, followed by the rest of us to the upper part of the field, where we could look over the hedge and see several fields *beyond*.

Example Sentences - Use today's words to complete the following sentences.

1. The children were never allowed _____ the garden fence without an adult.
2. There was a fine _____ covering the streets and obscuring their feet.
3. Many an unforeseen _____ occurred that holiday.
4. At the end of the path, I urged my horse forward and we _____ into an open field.
5. From behind the curtain she heard the audience _____ : "Bravo! Encore!"

Definitions - Write today's words next to their meanings.

1. An enthusiastic call or shout _____
2. Horses' pace of movement: slower than a gallop and faster than a trot

   _____
3. A situation, event or action _____
4. A cloud of water vapour suspended in the air near the ground

   _____
5. Outside or further away _____

Today's Idiom

to have all hands on deck
to have everyone available providing help

We need all hands on deck to decorate the room in time for the party.

Exercise 29

Today's Words

shuffled	nudging	decidedly	mysterious	glow

The Wind in the Willows – Kenneth Grahame

He *shuffled* on in front of them, carrying the light, and they followed him, *nudging* each other in an anticipating sort of way, down a long, gloomy, and, to tell the truth, *decidedly* shabby passage, into a sort of a central hall, out of which they could dimly see other long tunnel-like passages branching, passages *mysterious* and without apparent end. But there were doors in the hall as well – stout oaken comfortable-looking doors. One of these the Badger flung open, and at once they found themselves in all the *glow* and warmth of a large fire-lit kitchen.

Example Sentences - Use today's words to complete the following sentences.

1. Christmas shoppers hurried around to buy presents, _____ one another as they moved around the crowded store.
2. The forest looked magical, with the _____ of the fireflies lighting up every tree.
3. The whole thing was very _____ , no one knew what had happened to the boy.
4. The naughty children nervously _____ into the headmaster's office.
5. Doing more exercise had a _____ positive impact on his mood and his health.

Definitions - Write today's words next to their meanings.

1. Walked slowly dragging one's feet   _____
2. Undeniably, certainly   _____
3. Gently prodding or lightly touching someone or thing   _____
4. A steady radiance of light   _____
5. Difficult to explain or identify   _____

Today's Word Origin

evolve
The word originates from the Latin word **evolvere, e** meaning 'out of' and **volvere** meaning 'to roll'.

Exercise 30

Today's Words

lashed	lurched	mercy	flailing	crest

A Sea Crossing

The rain *lashed* down as the boat *lurched* dramatically from side to side. We clung desperately to whatever we could find, crying for *mercy* between the unforgiving blows of the sea. From the deck we could see nothing but the frozen blackness of the storm, illuminated briefly by great flashes of lightning. Flash! The helpless *flailing* of the torn rigging, lit by the bright, white light. Flash! The sails flapping, useless, against the mast. Flash! The *crest* of an enormous wave, bigger than any that had come before, looming above us.

Example Sentences - Use today's words to complete the following sentences.

1. They marched onwards until they reached the _____ of the hill.
2. All at once, the car _____ forward and they drove off down the road.
3. I ran through the forest as brambles and branches _____ my arms and legs.
4. The gladiator attacked fiercely and without _____ .
5. The flag was _____ madly in during the heavy winds.

Definitions - Write today's words next to their meanings.

1. The highest point of a mountain, hill or wave   _____
2. Beat forcefully   _____
3. Compassion or forgiveness   _____
4. Wild, uncontrolled waving or swinging   _____
5. Made an abrupt movement   _____

Today's Idiom

to bite somebody's head off
to react angrily to someone with little or no reason

"I only asked, there's no need to bite my head off."

Exercise 31

Today's Words

alternative	congested	envy	template	efficient

The London Underground

The London Underground is a public, mainly underground system of trains that serves Greater London and some areas of the neighbouring counties. An *alternative* name for the Underground is the Tube. It was the world's first underground railway with the first sections opening in 1863. Nowadays, it is the 11th busiest metro system in the world, so it can often get very *congested*. When it was first built it was the *envy* of many other major cities, including Paris and New York, who subsequently opened their own metro systems. The design of the London Underground map is famous the world over, and became the *template* for many other metro maps. Despite some delays, the system works well and is remarkably *efficient*, even at peak times.

Example Sentences - Use today's words to complete the following sentences.

1. The salad bar offered an _____ option to fast-food.
2. The original was used as a _____ to make multiple copies.
3. A road accident will often make the roads very _____ .
4. He was always very _____ with his work so that he could finish in good time.
5. Her brand new car made her the _____ of the other mothers.

Definitions - Write today's words next to their meanings.

1. Working in a productive, effective way _____
2. An outline or model _____
3. Another, equally valid, option _____
4. Crowded or blocked _____
5. Something which inspires jealousy in others _____

Today's Word Origin

local
*The word originates from the Latin word **locus** meaning 'place'.*

Exercise 32

Today's Words

especially	ambiguous	exceed	arrogant	willing

Setting Homework

A teacher who sets lots of homework is often very unpopular, *especially* if it means there is lots to be done over the weekend. It is always important that there is no question of when the homework is due, because students can always use an *ambiguous* due date as an excuse for not completing the work. There are always a few students who *exceed* expectations, and who get all the homework done quickly and correctly. However, no student should be too *arrogant* to check through their work, because even the best students make mistakes. All teachers know that any student that is *willing* to learn and work hard will make good progress.

Example Sentences - Use today's words to complete the following sentences.

1. The _____ tennis player expected to win every match.
2. It is illegal to _____ the speed limit.
3. The children were very polite, _____ when their grandmother was visiting.
4. He was always _____ to do more to help his friends.
5. Despite the task being a simple one, the instructions given were _____ .

Definitions - Write today's words next to their meanings.

1. Possessing an exaggerated opinion of one's own importance or abilities _____
2. Go beyond what is expected _____
3. Used to single out a particular situation above another _____
4. Unclear, open to interpretation _____
5. Ready or prepared to do something _____

Today's Idiom

to run around like a headless chicken
to be very busy doing lots of things in a disorganised way

She was running around like a headless chicken to get ready for work.

Exercise 33

Today's Words

troop	galloped	gait	rattling	castanets

King Solomon's Mines – H. Rider Haggard

As we emerged into this river-bed path suddenly we started a *troop* of tall giraffes, who *galloped*, or rather sailed off, in their strange *gait*, their tails screwed up over their backs, and their hoofs *rattling* like *castanets*.

Example Sentences - Use today's words to complete the following sentences.

1. He was concerned about the _____ sound coming from the car's engine.
2. The Spanish woman played the _____ as the flamenco music played.
3. The wild horses _____ across the plains.
4. We heard the _____ of musicians before we saw them march round the corner.
5. Nick's injury meant that for many years he had an unusual _____ .

Definitions - Write today's words next to their meanings.

1. Making a series of knocking sounds   _____
2. A group of people or animals   _____
3. A musical instrument consisting of a pair of concave wooden pieces

   _____

4. A person's manner of walking   _____
5. To run at speed   _____

Today's Word Origin

mansion
The word originates from the Latin word **mansio** *meaning 'place where someone stays'.*

Exercise 34

Today's Words

saundered	splendours	farthest	compact	ample

The Prince and the Pauper – Mark Twain

Tom got up hungry, and *sauntered* hungry away, but with his thoughts busy with the shadowy *splendours* of his night's dream. He wandered here and there in the city, hardly noticing where he was going. By and by he found himself at Temple Bar, the *farthest* from home he had ever travelled in that direction. He stopped and considered a moment, then fell into his imaginings again, and passed on outside the walls of London. The Strand had ceased to be a country road then, and regarded itself as a street, but by a strained construction; for, though there was a tolerably *compact* row of houses on one side of it, there were only some scattered great buildings on the other, these being palaces of rich nobles, with *ample* and beautiful grounds stretching to the river.

Example Sentences - Use today's words to complete the following sentences.

1. Sally's walk to school was the longest because she lived _____ from the school.
2. Tony found an _____ choice of books at his local library.
3. Leslie _____ across the street, whistling her favourite tune.
4. Her clothes were _____ and she managed to put all of them into one suitcase.
5. The Emperor was proud to show off the many _____ of his kingdom.

Definitions - Write today's words next to their meanings.

1. Enough or more than enough   _____
2. Situated at the greatest distance from a specified point   _____
3. Walked leisurely and in a relaxed manner   _____
4. Tightly packed together   _____
5. Magnificent and splendid things   _____

Today's Idiom

to be worlds apart
to be separated by a long distance or to hold very different views on a matter

Their opinions about their favourite films were worlds apart.

Exercise 35

Today's Words

holy	justly	learned	alms	reign

Young Folks' History of England – Charlotte Yonge

But Alfred was not only a brave warrior. He was a most good and *holy* man, who feared God above all things, and tried to do his very best for his people. He made good laws for them, and took care that everyone should be *justly* treated, and that nobody should do his neighbour wrong without being punished. He invited *learned* men from abroad, and wrote and translated books himself for them; and he had a school in his house, where he made the young nobles learn with his own sons. He built up the churches, and gave *alms* to the poor; and he was always ready to hear the troubles of any poor man. Though he was always working so hard, he had a disease that used to cause him terrible pain almost every day. His last years were less peaceful than the middle ones of his *reign*, for the Danes tried to come again; but he beat them off by his ships at sea, and when he died at fifty-two years old, in the year 901, he left England at rest and quiet, and we always think of him as one of the

Example Sentences - Use today's words to complete the following sentences.

1. The _____ of Queen Elizabeth I lasted 44 years.
2. My neighbour is a _____ man and often gives speeches at the local hall.
3. Church is a _____ place where Christians go to pray.
4. The wealthy lords and ladies were encouraged to give _____ to the poor.
5. In my school, teachers treat us _____ and with respect.

Definitions - Write today's words next to their meanings.

1. Well educated, knowledgeable _____
2. Religious, devoted or related to god _____
3. Charitable donations _____
4. Fairly, rightly _____
5. The period of time that a ruler is in power _____

Today's Word Origin

table
*The word originates from the Latin word **tabula** meaning 'board'. The word originally referred to a flat board, slab or surface which did not have legs.*

Exercise 36

Today's Words

monument	controversies	merits	outward	limbo

Richard Wagner – John R. Runciman

It is now one hundred years since Richard Wagner was born, thirty since he died. In every land he has his *monument* in one shape or another; his music-dramas can be heard all the world over; all the ancient *controversies* as to their *merits* or demerits have died down. The Bayreuth theatre, the *outward* and visible sign of his inner greatness, has risen to the point of its most splendid glory and lapsed into the *limbo* of tenth-rate things. Everyone who really cares for the art of music, and especially the art of opera (of which art music is by far the most important factor), has had ample time and opportunity for making up his mind.

Example Sentences - Use today's words to complete the following sentences.

1. The court case was in _____ for several weeks due to the jury's delay in making a decision.
2. The _____ appearance of the school building was charming, but inside it was rather shabby.
3. The council recently commissioned a new _____ to be carved out of stone.
4. We would all prefer to be judged on our _____ rather than our flaws.
5. There were a number of _____ related to the appointment of the new president.

Definitions - Write today's words next to their meanings.

1. From the outside, external _____
2. A statue or other structure created in memory of someone or something

   _____
3. Prolonged public disagreements _____
4. An uncertain period of awaiting an outcome _____
5. Good features or qualities _____

Today's Idiom

to give the all-clear
to give a signal that indicates there is no danger or threat

Once he gave the all-clear, the fire drill was over and we went inside.

Exercise 37

Today's Words

accustomed	solitary	sublime	temperament	scorn

The Life of Michelangelo Buonarroti – John Addington Symonds

We are *accustomed* to think of Michelangelo as a self-withdrawn and *solitary* worker, living for his art, avoiding the conflict of society, immersed in *sublime* imaginings. On the whole, this is a correct conception of the man. Many passages of his biography will show how little he actively shared the passions and contentions of the stirring times through which he moved. Yet his *temperament* exposed him to sudden outbursts of *scorn* and anger, which brought him now and then into violent collision with his neighbours.

Example Sentences - Use today's words to complete the following sentences.

1. She had a good _____ , and was always gentle and patient with others.
2. The group of protesters stared at the politician with _____ .
3. I went to view the _____ ceiling of the Sistine Chapel.
4. The boy was _____ to taking off his shoes before entering his house.
5. The old man lived a _____ life, in a lonely cottage on the moor.

Definitions - Write today's words next to their meanings.

1. Disdain, contempt   _____
2. Personality, nature   _____
3. Done alone, unaccompanied   _____
4. Very excellent or beautiful   _____
5. Used to, familiar with   _____

Today's Word Origin

vacation
*The word originates from the Latin word **vacare** meaning 'to be unoccupied'.*

Exercise 38

Today's Words

quality	possess	unhesitatingly	desirable	ingenuity

Camp and Trail – Stewart Edward White

Many people have asked me what, all things considered, is the most valuable *quality* a wilderness traveller can *possess*. Always I have replied *unhesitatingly*; for no matter how useful or *desirable* such attributes as patience, courage, strength, endurance, good nature, and *ingenuity*, may prove to be, undoubtedly a man with them but without the sense of direction, is practically helpless in the wilds.

Example Sentences - Use today's words to complete the following sentences.

1. Her determination was her greatest _____ and had helped to make her a successful businesswoman.
2. Sheila hired people with the _____ to develop new solutions and approaches.
3. It is always useful to _____ a good sense of humour in a difficult situation.
4. She knew exactly where to go and turned _____ down the little lane on the right.
5. A good pair of shoes is _____ when going for a long hike.

Definitions - Write today's words next to their meanings.

1. Acting without doubt or hesitation _____
2. An attribute or characteristic _____
3. Own or have _____
4. The quality of being inventive and original _____
5. Wished for, good to have _____

Today's Idiom

to get your knickers in a twist
to react too strongly to a difficult situation by getting angry or upset

"There's nothing to be upset about, don't get your knickers in a twist."

Exercise 39

Today's Words

| dismal | reluctantly | initiated | yield | fervently |

A Day at Home

Fiona felt *dismal*. She had a splitting headache, her throat felt like sandpaper, and her whole head was congested. *Reluctantly*, she picked up the telephone and called her workplace to tell them that she couldn't go in. She had been so looking forward to today; the experiment that she had *initiated* a couple of months ago would finally *yield* some results. Fiona closed her eyes and *fervently* willed someone reliable to collect the data for her, in the hope that she would be well enough tomorrow to go in and sort everything out.

Example Sentences - Use today's words to complete the following sentences.

1. The boy _____ wished that his dear father would be home for Christmas.
2. Investments in technology _____ more money than any other industry.
3. The grey, thunderous clouds made for a _____ day at the beach.
4. The children tidied their rooms _____ , as they would rather be playing.
5. They were pleased to have _____ the book-borrowing scheme because the children loved it so much.

Definitions - Write today's words next to their meanings.

1. To produce or generate   _____
2. With great intensity   _____
3. Gloomy, uninspiring or pitiful   _____
4. Started up or set in motion   _____
5. Without willingness   _____

┌─ Today's Word Origin ──────────────────────────────

man

*The root **manu** is from the ancient Indian language of Sanskrit, referring to the first man, or the father of all humanity.*

Exercise 40

Today's Words

leagues	likewise	rumoured	asserted	extreme

Notable Voyagers – W.H.G. Kingston and Henry Frith

A Portuguese pilot, Martin Vicenti, after sailing four hundred and fifty-two *leagues* to the west of Cape Saint Vincent, had found a piece of carved wood evidently laboured with an iron instrument, and as probably the wind had drifted it from the west, it might have come from some unknown land in that direction. A brother-in-law of Columbus had *likewise* found a similar piece of wood drifted from the same quarter. Reeds of enormous size, such as were described by Ptolemy to grow in India, had been picked up, and trunks of huge pine trees had been driven on the shores of the Azores, such as did not grow on any of those islands. The bodies of two dead men, whose features differed from those of any known race of people, had been cast on the island of Flores. There were islands, it was *rumoured*, still farther west than those visited, and a mariner sailing from Port Saint Mary to Ireland *asserted* that he had seen land to the west, which the ship's company took to be some *extreme* point of Tartary.

Example Sentences - Use today's words to complete the following sentences.

1. It is _____ that there are ways to turn iron into gold.
2. He began to run faster, and if she wanted to keep up, she would _____ have to increase her speed.
3. He enjoyed living in cold wild places, so he built a house in the _____ north of Scotland.
4. The submarine went four _____ under the sea.
5. The shopkeeper _____ that he saw two men stealing a car on Saturday.

Definitions - Write today's words next to their meanings.

1. Measures of distance at or under the sea _____
2. A statement or idea which has been spread between people _____
3. Stated confidently _____
4. Furthest end, outermost _____
5. In the same way, also _____

> **Today's Idiom**
>
> ### a laughing stock
> *a person who makes a fool of themselves, so that everyone laughs at or mocks them*
>
> **He was the laughing stock of the school after forgetting his trousers.**

Exercise 41

Today's Words

spray	trivial	import	expression	siege

The Picture of Dorian Gray – Oscar Wilde

Dorian Gray listened, open-eyed and wondering. The *spray* of lilac fell from his hand upon the gravel. A furry bee came and buzzed round it for a moment. Then it began to scramble all over the oval stellated globe of the tiny blossoms. He watched it with that strange interest in *trivial* things that we try to develop when things of high *import* make us afraid, or when we are stirred by some new emotion for which we cannot find *expression*, or when some thought that terrifies us lays sudden *siege* to the brain and calls on us to yield. After a time the bee flew away.

Example Sentences - Use today's words to complete the following sentences.

1. He pinned a _____ of white blooms to his jacket for the wedding.
2. She hated it when people asked her _____ questions when she was busy with important things.
3. The _____ of his actions were only understood later.
4. The city was under _____ by the Romans.
5. She gave him the gift as an _____ of her love for him.

Definitions - Write today's words next to their meanings.

1. Meaning, consequence, significance   _____
2. A small stem or branch with flowers or foliage   _____
3. Effort to take over or overcome resistance of something   _____
4. A way of showing or saying something   _____
5. Not important or relevant   _____

Today's Word Origin

caravan
The word originates from the Persian word **kārwān** *meaning 'convoy'.*

Exercise 42

Today's Words

instinct	dash	unexplainable	suburban	disguise

The Magic City – Edith Nesbit

And so, at last, they came close to Polistopolis. Philip never could tell how it was that he stopped the car outside the city. It must have been some quite unaccountable *instinct*, because naturally, you know, when you are not used to being driven in motors, you like to *dash* up to the house you are going to, and enjoy your friends' enjoyment of the grand way in which you have travelled. But Philip felt—in that quite certain and quite *unexplainable* way in which you do feel things sometimes—that it was best to stop the car among the *suburban* groves of southernwood, and to creep into the town in the *disguise* afforded by motor coats, motor veils and motor goggles.

Example Sentences - Use today's words to complete the following sentences.

1. Sally was usually late, and would often have to _____ to the bus stop.
2. When Roma heard the gunshot, her first _____ was to run.
3. When something _____ happens, it is normal to want to find an answer.
4. Spies will often wear a _____ so they cannot be recognised.
5. I live in a small _____ town not far from Birmingham.

Definitions - Write today's words next to their meanings.

1. Unable to be explained or accounted for   _____
2. Move in a hurry   _____
3. A natural response made without thinking, a gut reaction   _____
4. A false appearance used to hide a true identity   _____
5. Of a residential area surrounding a city   _____

Today's Idiom

a loose cannon
a person who behaves unpredictably and potentially causes problems for others

She was a loose cannon and couldn't be trusted to show up.

Exercise 43

Today's Words

natural	punctual	delights	herds	foe

The Railway Children – Edith Nesbit

It was one day when Mother had gone to Maidbridge. She had gone alone, but the children were to go to the station to meet her. And, loving the station as they did, it was only *natural* that they should be there a good hour before there was any chance of Mother's train arriving, even if the train were *punctual*, which was most unlikely. No doubt they would have been just as early, even if it had been a fine day, and all the *delights* of woods and fields and rocks and rivers had been open to them. But it happened to be a very wet day and, for July, very cold. There was a wild wind that drove flocks of dark purple clouds across the sky 'like *herds* of dream-elephants', as Phyllis said. And the rain stung sharply, so that the way to the station was finished at a run. Then the rain fell faster and harder, and beat slantwise against the windows of the booking office and of the chill place that had General Waiting Room on its door.

'It's like being in a besieged castle,' Phyllis said; 'look at the arrows of the *foe* striking against the battlements!'

Example Sentences - Use today's words to complete the following sentences.

1. I looked beyond the camp and saw _____ of wildebeest crossing the river.
2. It is polite and helpful to make a habit of always being _____ .
3. The boxer took a deep breath and prepared to face his _____ .
4. It was _____ for the girls to miss their parents while they were away at camp.
5. The family made sure to enjoy all the _____ of the holiday camp.

Definitions - Write today's words next to their meanings.

1. In accordance with normal behaviour_____
2. An enemy or opponent   _____
3. Elements that cause pleasure   _____
4. On time   _____
5. Groups of animals   _____

Today's Word Origin

lollipop
*The word originates from the late 18th century word **lolly** meaning 'tongue'.*

Exercise 44

Today's Words

voyages	warfare	notorious	raids	monasteries

The Vikings

The Vikings were sea-travellers of Northern European origin who undertook *voyages* from the late 8th century to the 11th century. As traders, explorers and warriors, they sailed the seas in longships, which were designed for *warfare* and exploration. They were *notorious* for violent *raids* on unsuspecting towns and villages, which they carried out throughout Europe and beyond. In Medieval England, Vikings were known as 'Northmen' or 'Norsemen', and they attacked Christian *monasteries*, burned books, stole precious treasures and murdered monks.

Example Sentences - Use today's words to complete the following sentences.

1. The 'Blitz' was a term used for the frequent bombing _____ that were carried out over Britain in World War II.
2. Everyone knew the outlaw, he was _____ for smuggling goods across the border.
3. He was a good sailor and had made many _____ .
4. Typically, _____ have only basic facilities, as monks choose to live simply.
5. Modern _____ has changed a great deal since the Ancient Greeks attacked Troy.

Definitions - Write today's words next to their meanings.

1. Journeys involving travel by sea _____
2. Well-known or famous for a bad reason _____
3. The activities involved in war _____
4. Buildings inhabited by communities of monks _____
5. Sudden, surprise attacks _____

Today's Idiom

to take matters into your own hands
to deal with something yourself because some has failed to, or has done it badly

She took matters into her own hands and completed the group project.

Exercise 45

Today's Words

| employed | enforce | established | symbol | oppression |

The Police

Police officers are *employed* by the state to *enforce* the law. Policing was a recognised career in Ancient Rome and China, but the first *established* police force was not created until 1667, in Paris, where it aimed to ensure peace and quiet, as well as to maintain the class system. Soon after, police forces had been established in most French towns. The concept of policing then travelled to England where it was strongly disliked as it was seen as a *symbol* of *oppression*.

Example Sentences - Use today's words to complete the following sentences.

1. The uniform became a _____ of everything she hated about her school.
2. The manager _____ three people to supervise the other members of staff.
3. Our company has offices _____ in cities all over the world.
4. The _____ of citizens because of their religion or race is illegal.
5. Superheroes _____ justice.

Definitions - Write today's words next to their meanings.

1. Ensure an idea or rule is carried out   _____
2. Paid to do a job   _____
3. Prolonged unjust treatment   _____
4. An object which represents an idea   _____
5. Existing for an extended period of time   _____

Today's Word Origin

volcano
The word originates from Roman mythology, in which **Vulcan** was the god of fire and volcanoes.

Exercise 46

Today's Words

waltzed	pounded	cumbersome	tremendous	gleaming

A Cricket Match

The time had come for John to show everyone what he had learnt. He picked up the bat and *waltzed* over to the white lines. The sun's rays *pounded* own onto the ground and the grass began to sweat. John drew in a long, deep breath and felt the air move through his lungs, like water flooding into the driest river. His helmet dug into the back of his head and his pads were *cumbersome*, but he was ready. In a flash, the bowler was running at him with *tremendous* speed, the sun *gleaming* off the ball. It was only when John saw the umpire raise his finger that he realised he was out.

Example Sentences - Use today's words to complete the following sentences.

1. She wanted to do a good job, so she polished the brass until it was

   _____ .

2. Given the emergency, Tim _____ on door and woke up the neighbours.

3. There was a _____ amount of food on the table, its legs were nearly groaning.

4. His pockets were so full of sweets that his coat was becoming _____ .

5. She _____ up to the counter and ordered two coffees.

Definitions - Write today's words next to their meanings.

1. Large or heavy in way that is difficult to use   _____
2. Shining with reflected light   _____
3. Moved casually and confidently   _____
4. To repeatedly strike   _____
5. Very great in amount or intensity   _____

Today's Idiom

to go the extra mile
to put special effort into something

He went the extra mile and cooked a three course meal for Mother's Day.

Exercise 47

Today's Words

unpredictable	subsequently	experience	nature	prolonged

British Weather

The weather in Britain is renowned for being *unpredictable*. A wet, grey morning can *subsequently* change into a bright, warm afternoon. No amount of *experience* can make it easier to guess what the weather will be like. More often than not, however, it is likely to rain. Even in the warmer months, the *nature* of the weather means that the British people must be prepared for anything. More and more frequently, summers will see *prolonged*, heavy rain when many parts of the country are damaged by flooding.

Example Sentences - Use today's words to complete the following sentences.

1. He was given very clear instructions in the morning but _____ disobeyed them.
2. The guard-dog outside the bank had a strangely cowardly _____ .
3. The future is entirely _____ , despite the claims of soothsayers.
4. The tennis player was reprimanded for having _____ the match.
5. He clearly had a lot of _____ with using computers, so he was offered the job.

Definitions - Write today's words next to their meanings.

1. Not able to be foreseen   _____
2. Natural features or qualities   _____
3. Afterwards, following   _____
4. Continued for a long period of time   _____
5. Knowledge and skill in a particular activity   _____

--- Today's Word Origin ---

acrobat
*The word originates from the Greek word **akcrobatos** meaning 'walking on tiptoe',
since the earliest acrobats were tightrope walkers.*

Exercise 48

Today's Words

briskly	whisked	midst	evidently	servitude

The Wonderful Wizard of Oz – L. Frank Baum

There were several roads nearby, but it did not take her long to find the one paved with yellow bricks. Within a short time she was walking *briskly* toward the Emerald City, her silver shoes tinkling merrily on the hard, yellow road-bed. The sun shone bright and the birds sang sweetly, and Dorothy did not feel nearly so bad as you might think a little girl would who had been suddenly *whisked* away from her own country and set down in the *midst* of a strange land.

She was surprised, as she walked along, to see how pretty the country was about her. There were neat fences at the sides of the road, painted a dainty blue colour, and beyond them were fields of grain and vegetables in abundance. *Evidently* the Munchkins were good farmers and able to raise large crops. Once in a while she would pass a house, and the people came out to look at her and bow low as she went by; for everyone knew she had been the means of destroying the Wicked Witch and setting them free from *servitude*.

Example Sentences - Use today's words to complete the following sentences.

1. The entire cake had been devoured, _____ the children liked chocolate.
2. It was a cold day so Thomas walked _____ , and also he was running late.
3. The young boy found himself in the _____ of a great crowd.
4. They were forced to cross the sea and live a life of _____ .
5. As a surprise, his wife had _____ him off to Paris for the weekend.

Definitions - Write today's words next to their meanings.

1. In the middle of   _____
2. Obviously, in a way that has been proven   _____
3. The state of being a slave   _____
4. Quickly and with energy   _____
5. Take someone or something away quickly without warning   _____

Today's Idiom

to get away with murder
to do something very wrong without being punished or caught

She's such cheeky girl, she gets away with murder.

Exercise 49

Today's Words

cyclone	stately	luscious	plumage	rushing

The Wonderful Wizard of Oz – L. Frank Baum

The *cyclone* had set the house down very gently – for a cyclone – in the midst of a country of marvellous beauty. There were lovely patches of greensward all about, with *stately* trees bearing rich and *luscious* fruits. Banks of gorgeous flowers were on every hand, and birds with rare and brilliant *plumage* sang and fluttered in the trees and bushes. A little way off was a small brook, *rushing* and sparkling along between green banks, and murmuring in a voice very grateful to a little girl who had lived so long on the dry, grey prairies.

Example Sentences - Use today's words to complete the following sentences.

1. At the zoo, Zara saw many peacocks, each showcasing their colourful

   _____ .

2. All the villagers were _____ to the annual fête.
3. The people of the town heard there was a _____ approaching and boarded up the windows.
4. Sweet juice trickled down his finger as he ate the _____ peach.
5. The lord planned to build a _____ home in his park.

Definitions - Write today's words next to their meanings.

1. Moving with urgent haste _____
2. All the feathers of a bird _____
3. A storm consisting of rotating winds _____
4. Having a rich, sweet taste _____
5. Impressive or grand in size, appearance or manner _____

Today's Word Origin

innocent
*The word originates from the Latin words **in** means 'not' and **nocere** means 'to hurt, injure'.*

Exercise 50

Today's Words

exhaustion	goaded	rein	confusion	pitiful

Black Beauty – Anna Sewell

I got along fairly till we came to Ludgate Hill; but there the heavy load and my own *exhaustion* were too much. I was struggling to keep on, *goaded* by constant chucks of the *rein* and use of the whip, when in a single moment - I cannot tell how - my feet slipped from under me, and I fell heavily to the ground on my side; the suddenness and the force with which I fell seemed to beat all the breath out of my body. I lay perfectly still; indeed, I had no power to move, and I thought I now was going to die. I heard a sort of *confusion* round me, loud, angry voices, and the getting down of the luggage, but it was all like a dream. I thought I heard that sweet, *pitiful* voice saying, "Oh! that poor horse! It is all our fault."

Example Sentences - Use today's words to complete the following sentences.

1. On the first day of school, the twins caused a lot of _____ amongst the teachers.
2. Holly grasped the _____ tightly as the horse galloped over the fence.
3. After a long, tiring day at work, he was overwhelmed by _____ .
4. The bullies _____ the girl into running away from school.
5. When John fell over, his mother let out a _____ noise.

Definitions - Write today's words next to their meanings.

1. Uncertainty about what is happening   _____
2. Compassionate, pitying   _____
3. A long, leather strap used to guide a horse   _____
4. Provoked or annoyed   _____
5. A state of extreme tiredness   _____

Today's Idiom

to stick your nose into something
to pry or interfere in the business of other people

He has a bad habit of sticking his nose into other people's business.

BLANK PAGE

Answers

Answers

Example Exercise	Example Sentences	Definitions
	1. estate	1. bitterly
	2. defeated	2. estate
	3. bitterly	3. unsparingly
	4. traitors	4. defeated
	5. unsparingly	5. traitor

Exercise 1	Example Sentences	Definitions
	1. sparkling	1. wondering
	2. studded	2. tint
	3. dazzled	3. studded
	4. tint	4. sparkling
	5. wondering	5. dazzled

Exercise 2	Example Sentences	Definitions
	1. bare	1. rusty
	2. loose	2. shone
	3. rusty	3. bare
	4. lovely	4. loose
	5. shone	5. lovely

Exercise 3	Example Sentences	Definitions
	1. rigging	1. stirring
	2. shimmering	2. mild
	3. cabin	3. rigging
	4. stirring	4. shimmering
	5. mild	5. cabin

Exercise 4	Example Sentences	Definitions
	1. underbrush	1. wilder
	2. disagreeable	2. muddy
	3. wilder	3. disagreeable
	4. bogs	4. bogs
	5. muddy	5. underbrush

Exercise 5	Example Sentences	Definitions
	1. divided	1. jagged
	2. jagged	2. ditch
	3. ditch	3. steep
	4. steep	4. eventful
	5. eventful	5. divided

Exercise 6	Example Sentences	Definitions
	1. bent	1. ought
	2. pleasant	2. bent
	3. ought	3. temper
	4. strapped	4. strapped
	5. temper	5. pleasant

Answers

Exercise 7	Example Sentences	Definitions
	1. grown	1. dirty
	2. dirty	2. scratch
	3. content	3. content
	4. roosted	4. grown
	5. scratch	5. roosted

Exercise 8	Example Sentences	Definitions
	1. reckless	1. wounded
	2. bold	2. inky
	3. inky	3. bold
	4. wounded	4. markings
	5. markings	5. reckless

Exercise 9	Example Sentences	Definitions
	1. outstanding	1. hamper
	2. ordinary	2. ordinary
	3. creative	3. substantial
	4. hamper	4. creative
	5. substantial	5. outstanding

Exercise 10	Example Sentences	Definitions
	1. lavish	1. stresses
	2. stresses	2. festive
	3. sociable	3. lavish
	4. snug	4. sociable
	5. festive	5. snug

Exercise 11	Example Sentences	Definitions
	1. sane	1. majority
	2. virtuous	2. virtuous
	3. distinct	3. distinct
	4. majority	4. sane
	5. educated	5. educated

Exercise 12	Example Sentences	Definitions
	1. medieval	1. monk
	2. monk	2. grievous
	3. rich	3. residence
	4. residence	4. medieval
	5. grievous	5. rich

Exercise 13	Example Sentences	Definitions
	1. shrubbery	1. rustle
	2. steadily	2. steadily
	3. expedition	3. shrubbery
	4. rustle	4. decay
	5. decay	5. expedition

Answers

	Example Sentences	Definitions
Exercise 14	1. puzzled 2. furrow 3. conclusion 4. succeeded 5. provoking	1. conclusion 2. succeeded 3. furrow 4. puzzled 5. provoking

	Example Sentences	Definitions
Exercise 15	1. timid 2. pattering 3. violently 4. trotting 5. savage	1. pattering 2. savage 3. timid 4. violently 5. trotting

	Example Sentences	Definitions
Exercise 16	1. pretending 2. advice 3. croquet 4. scolded 5. fond	1. fond 2. pretending 3. croquet 4. advice 5. scolded

	Example Sentences	Definitions
Exercise 17	1. polished 2. bore 3. mortal 4. blushing 5. exceedingly	1. polished 2. bore 3. mortal 4. exceedingly 5. blushing

	Example Sentences	Definitions
Exercise 18	1. obedient 2. meek 3. lords 4. proclaimed 5. oaths	1. proclaimed 2. oaths 3. obedient 4. lords 5. meek

	Example Sentences	Definitions
Exercise 19	1. embroidered 2. trailing 3. velvet 4. fastened 5. honour	1. honour 2. velvet 3. embroidered 4. trailing 5. fastened

	Example Sentences	Definitions
Exercise 20	1. hunt 2. tend 3. beams 4. curled 5. flitted	1. curled 2. tend 3. hunt 4. beams 5. flitted

Answers

Exercise 21	Example Sentences	Definitions
	1. praised	1. feebly
	2. feebly	2. cocoa
	3. cocoa	3. resisted
	4. devoted	4. devoted
	5. resisted	5. praised

Exercise 22	Example Sentences	Definitions
	1. awesome	1. molten
	2. eruption	2. ash
	3. molten	3. awesome
	4. ash	4. eruption
	5. inhabitants	5. inhabitants

Exercise 23	Example Sentences	Definitions
	1. limbs	1. escort
	2. glimpses	2. glimpses
	3. jerk	3. limbs
	4. escort	4. jerk
	5. giddy	5. giddy

Exercise 24	Example Sentences	Definitions
	1. wonders	1. dragged
	2. dragged	2. dear
	3. draughty	3. wonders
	4. shivered	4. draughty
	5. dear	5. shivered

Exercise 25	Example Sentences	Definitions
	1. possessions	1. achieve
	2. achieve	2. tombs
	3. buried	3. buried
	4. prepare	4. prepare
	5. tombs	5. possessions

Exercise 26	Example Sentences	Definitions
	1. fading	1. fading
	2. retired	2. bittersweet
	3. bittersweet	3. squeal
	4. squeal	4. sigh
	5. sigh	5. retired

Exercise 27	Example Sentences	Definitions
	1. unsteady	1. plainly
	2. hopeless	2. hopeless
	3. chestnut	3. unsteady
	4. plainly	4. dull
	5. dull	5. chestnut

Answers

	Example Sentences	Definitions
Exercise 28	1. beyond 2. mist 3. circumstance 4. cantered 5. cry	1. cry 2. cantered 3. circumstance 4. mist 5. beyond
Exercise 29	1. nudging 2. glow 3. mysterious 4. shuffled 5. decidedly	1. shuffled 2. decidedly 3. nudging 4. glow 5. mysterious
Exercise 30	1. crest 2. lurched 3. lashed 4. mercy 5. flailing	1. crest 2. lashed 3. mercy 4. flailing 5. lurched
Exercise 31	1. alternative 2. template 3. congested 4. efficient 5. envy	1. efficient 2. template 3. alternative 4. congested 5. envy
Exercise 32	1. arrogant 2. exceed 3. especially 4. willing 5. ambiguous	1. arrogant 2. exceed 3. especially 4. ambiguous 5. willing
Exercise 33	1. rattling 2. castanets 3. galloped 4. troop 5. gait	1. rattling 2. troop 3. castanets 4. gait 5. galloped
Exercise 34	1. farthest 2. ample 3. sauntered 4. compact 5. splendours	1. ample 2. farthest 3. sauntered 4. compact 5. splendours

Answers

	Example Sentences	Definitions
Exercise 35	1. reign 2. learned 3. holy 4. alms 5. justly	1. learned 2. holy 3. alms 4. justly 5. reign

	Example Sentences	Definitions
Exercise 36	1. limbo 2. outward 3. monument 4. merits 5. controversies	1. outward 2. monument 3. controversies 4. limbo 5. merits

	Example Sentences	Definitions
Exercise 37	1. temperament 2. scorn 3. sublime 4. accustomed 5. solitary	1. scorn 2. temperament 3. solitary 4. sublime 5. accustomed

	Example Sentences	Definitions
Exercise 38	1. quality 2. ingenuity 3. possess 4. unhesitatingly 5. desirable	1. unhesitatingly 2. quality 3. possess 4. ingenuity 5. desirable

	Example Sentences	Definitions
Exercise 39	1. fervently 2. yield 3. dismal 4. reluctantly 5. initiated	1. yield 2. fervently 3. dismal 4. initiated 5. reluctantly

	Example Sentences	Definitions
Exercise 40	1. rumoured 2. likewise 3. extreme 4. leagues 5. asserted	1. leagues 2. rumoured 3. asserted 4. extreme 5. likewise

	Example Sentences	Definitions
Exercise 41	1. spray 2. trivial 3. import 4. siege 5. expression	1. import 2. spray 3. siege 4. expression 5. trivial

Answers

	Example Sentences	Definitions
Exercise 42	1. dash 2. instinct 3. unexplainable 4. disguise 5. suburban	1. unexplainable 2. dash 3. instinct 4. disguise 5. suburban
Exercise 43	1. herds 2. punctual 3. foe 4. natural 5. delights	1. natural 2. foe 3. delights 4. punctual 5. herds
Exercise 44	1. raids 2. notorious 3. voyages 4. monasteries 5. warfare	1. voyages 2. notorious 3. warfare 4. monasteries 5. raids
Exercise 45	1. symbol 2. employed 3. established 4. oppression 5. enforce	1. enforce 2. employed 3. oppression 4. symbol 5. established
Exercise 46	1. gleaming 2. pounded 3. tremendous 4. cumbersome 5. waltzed	1. cumbersome 2. gleaming 3. waltzed 4. pounded 5. tremendous
Exercise 47	1. subsequently 2. nature 3. unpredictable 4. prolonged 5. experience	1. unpredictable 2. nature 3. subsequently 4. prolonged 5. experience
Exercise 48	1. evidently 2. briskly 3. midst 4. servitude 5. whisked	1. midst 2. evidently 3. servitude 4. briskly 5. whisked

Answers

Exercise 49	Example Sentences	Definitions
	1. plumage	1. rushing
	2. rushing	2. plumage
	3. cyclone	3. cyclone
	4. luscious	4. luscious
	5. stately	5. stately

Exercise 50	Example Sentences	Definitions
	1. confusion	1. confusion
	2. rein	2. pitiful
	3. exhaustion	3. rein
	4. goaded	4. goaded
	5. pitiful	5. exhaustion

BLANK PAGE